ANYA'S GHOST

VERA BROSGOL

First Second

NEW YORK & LONDON

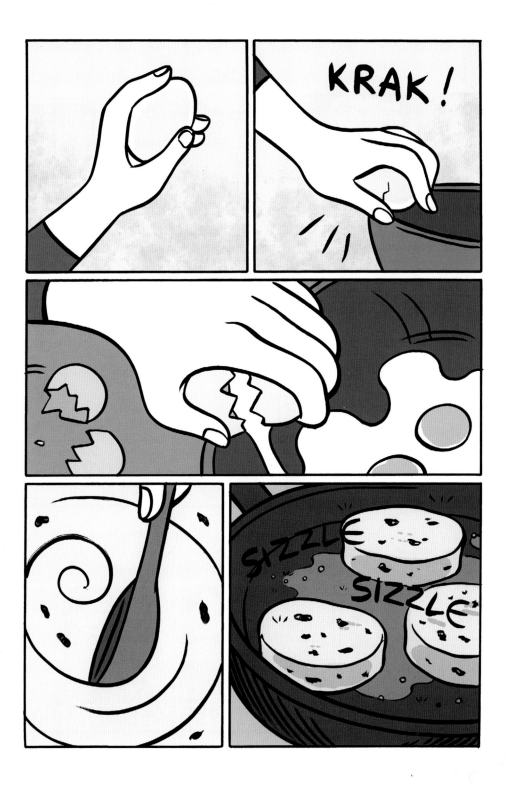

2

3

4

8

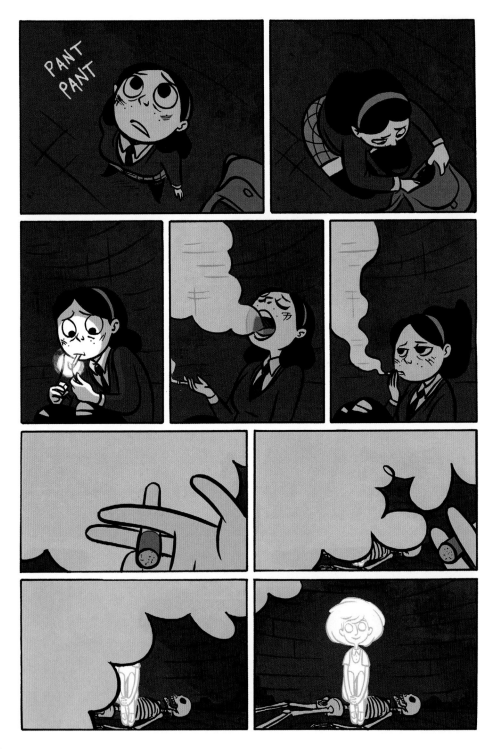

PANT
PANT

22

26

28

49

72

78

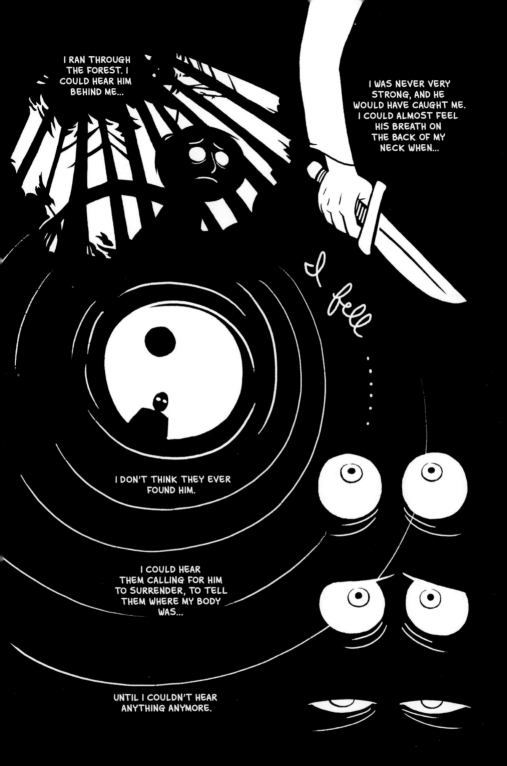

103

108

III

143

144

148

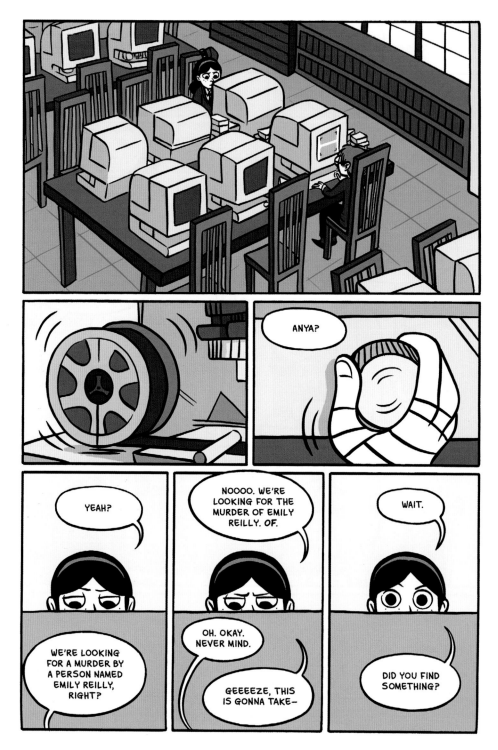

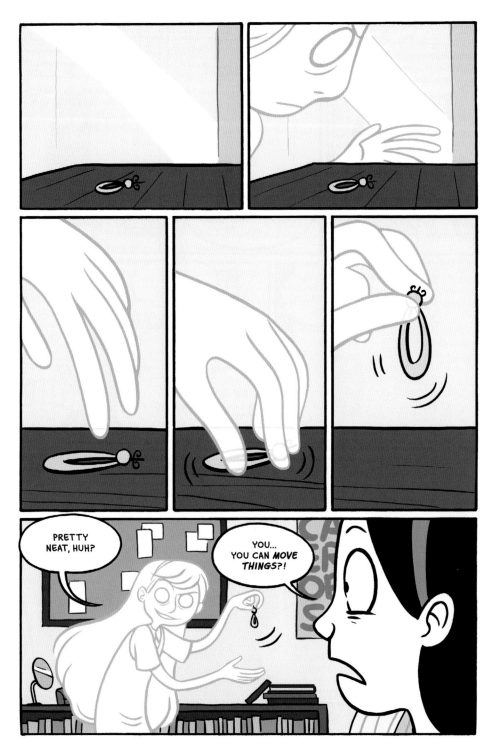

174

182

183

WHIMPER

199

the end.

First Second
NEW YORK & LONDON

THANKS TO: JUDY HANSEN, JEN WANG, GRAHAM ANNABLE,
RAINA TELGEMEIER, HOPE LARSON, AMY KIM AND KAZU
KIBUISHI, NEIL BABRA, SCOTT MCCLOUD, JEREMY SPAKE,
THE LOVELY FOLKS AT :01, AND MY MOM.

COPYRIGHT © 2011 BY VERA BROSGOL
PUBLISHED BY FIRST SECOND
FIRST SECOND IS AN IMPRINT OF ROARING BROOK PRESS,
A DIVISION OF HOLTZBRINCK PUBLISHING HOLDINGS LIMITED PARTNERSHIP,
175 FIFTH AVENUE, NEW YORK, NY 10010

ALL RIGHTS RESERVED

DISTRIBUTED IN THE UNITED KINGDOM BY MACMILLAN CHILDREN'S BOOKS,
A DIVISION OF PAN MACMILLAN.

DESIGN BY COLLEEN AF VENABLE

TYPE SET IN "HELVERICA," DESIGNED BY JOHN MARTZ.

CATALOGING-IN-PUBLICATION DATA IS ON FILE AT THE LIBRARY OF CONGRESS.

ISBN: 978-1-59643-770-8

FIRST SECOND BOOKS ARE AVAILABLE FOR SPECIAL PROMOTIONS AND PREMIUMS.
FOR DETAILS, CONTACT: DIRECTOR OF SPECIAL MARKETS, HOLTZBRINCK PUBLISHERS.

FIRST EDITION 2011
PRINTED IN CHINA

1 3 5 7 9 10 8 6 4 2